Willow and Her magic Owl Pillow

written By **Fiona Scott**

Illustrated by **Mariëtte Martin**

A stupen... ...fro... Silverwood

Published in 2017 by Silverwood Books

SilverWood Books Ltd
14 Small Street, Bristol, BS1 1DE, United Kingdom
www.silverwoodbooks.co.uk

Copyright © Fiona Scott 2017
Illustrations by Mariëtte Martin

ISBN 978-1-78132-671-8

British Library Cataloguing in Publication Data
A CIP catalogue record for this book is available from the British Library

Page design and typesetting by SilverWood Books
Printed on responsibly sourced paper

SilverWood

For Willow, our dancing girl

Willow loved to dance.
On Monday Willow did the hula in the hall.
On Tuesday Willow did ballet in the bathroom.
On Wednesday Willow did tap dancing on the toilet.

On Thursday Willow did street dance in the sitting room.
On Friday she did the can-can in the conservatory.

On Saturday Willow did ballroom in her bedroom and on Sunday she did disco dancing on the decking, with the sun as her disco ball.

But when it started to rain Willow had to go indoors.

She sat by the window with her favourite owl pillow and waited for the rain to stop.

There was a knock at the door. It was Willow's nana, Jackie!

Nana loved to dance, just like Willow. She told Willow about how she used to dance as a little girl and all the different styles of dance from when she was younger.

Willow wished she could do the dances and hear the music and see the outfits that Nana had told her about.

That night, after Nana went home, Willow lay down on her bed surrounded by her teddies and pillows and fell into a musical daydream. Suddenly she saw something move. It was her owl pillow. It winked at her!

The owl spoke. "If you squeeze my tummy I will take you on a musical adventure. Come on, let's go!"

Willow squeezed the pillow. To her surprise it made a magical, musical **whooooosh** and their adventure began...

In the blink of an eye they were in the 1920s. "This is jazz music," said the owl. The ladies and gentlemen of the Roaring Twenties were doing a dance called the Charleston. The ladies wore loose sparkly dresses with pretty headbands and the men wore fancy black suits.

The owl told Willow that people were also doing dances called the Shimmy, the Turkey Trot and the Bunny Hug. Willow joined in and laughed as she trotted like a turkey. "It's time to go," said the owl and **whooooosh** they were in a new place.

They were in the 1950s. Willow could see girls wearing big skirts with frilly petticoats and boys in different coloured suits. A handsome man with a quiff was swaying on stage. Everyone was dancing, mostly in pairs. "They are doing the Jitterbug and the Bop," explained the owl. Willow joined in, twisting her hips.

"This is Elvis, the king of rock and roll music," said the owl.

"It's time to go again," said the owl and **whooooosh** they were in a new place.

They were in the 1970s in a discotheque. A big silver disco ball spun from the ceiling and the squares on the dance floor lit up.

"This is disco music," said the owl. Ladies with big hair and tight colourful clothes were dancing with men in wide flared trousers. "They are doing the Funky Chicken and the YMCA," explained the owl. Willow joined in but as she was making the letters YMCA above her head the owl said, "It's time to go again," and **whooooosh** they were in a new place.

They were in the 1980s on MTV. "This is pop music," said the owl. There was a lady with lacy gloves and bright red lips, and a man in a red suit and black hat. "His name is Michael Jackson and her name is Madonna. They are the king and queen of pop music." People were wearing bright colours and doing dance moves like the Worm and the Moonwalk. Willow was doing her best Worm when the owl said, "It's time to go again," and **whooooosh** they were in a new place.

17

They were in the 1990s. "This is 90s pop. Meet Sporty, Scary, Baby, Posh and Ginger Spice," said the owl.

Willow jumped up and said, "And Willow Spice!" and with that she became the sixth Spice Girl. They did the 'Wannabe' dance and Willow learnt all about girl power. As she was making a peace sign with her fingers the owl said, "It's time to go again...this time to somewhere extra special," and **whooooosh** they were in a new place.

They were in the future...the 2090s. Willow could hear high-pitched electronic sounds. She saw alien ladies wearing helter-skelter dresses. "This is called moon-hop music," explained the owl.

There were aliens and astronauts dancing together, doing the real Moonwalk and the Spaceship Jig. Willow joined in and floated around with an alien who was on holiday from Jupiter.

"It's nearly time to go home," said the owl.

"No!" cried Willow. "I want to stay and dance on the moon forever."

But the adventure was over. The next thing Willow knew she was back on her bed. The owl whispered, "Home sweet home!"

Willow sat up and looked around. What a musical adventure that had been! She felt very tired from all the dancing and slowly fell asleep with a big smile on her face and slightly sore feet.

"Sweet dreams, dancing girl," the owl said with a wink. "Until next time!"

Lightning Source UK Ltd.
Milton Keynes UK
UKRC01n2142300717
306279UK00005B/57